MARVEL
AVENGERS

500
Stickers

Autumn
Publishing

AVENGERS ASSEMBLE

The Avengers are always ready for action. Can you spot the close-ups from the panel in the big battle scene?

A

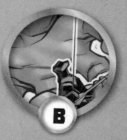

B

C

D

E

F

Answers on page 30

BLACK PANTHER POSES

King T'Challa is practising his awesome martial arts moves. Draw lines to link each pose to its pair and circle the pose that's on its own.

Answers on page 30

TOP TEAMS

To battle the bad guys, the Avengers are teaming up. Follow the lines to find out who will be working together today.

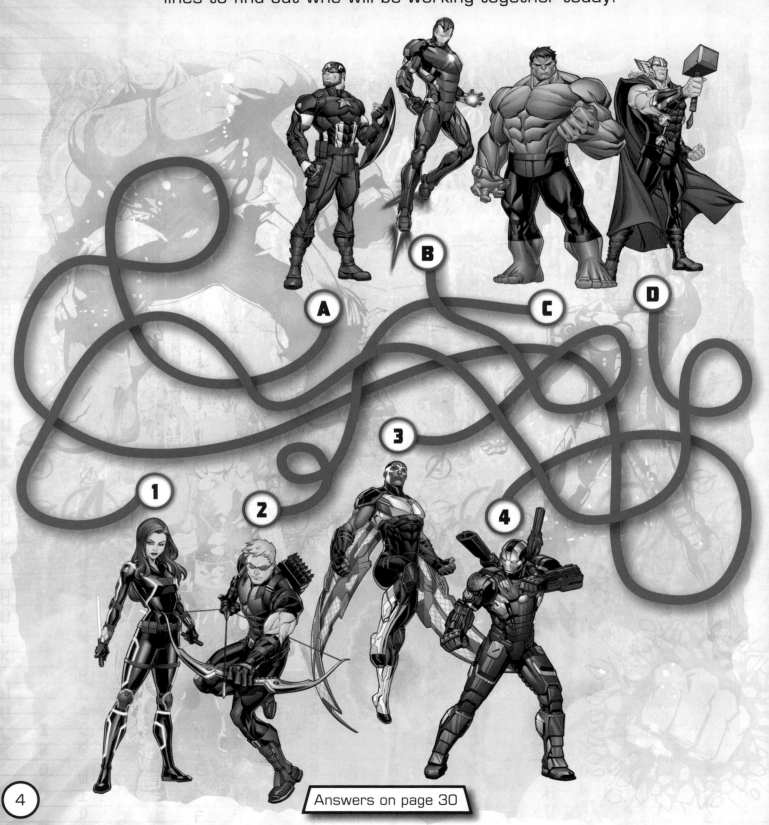

Answers on page 30

FROM ANT-MAN TO GIANT-MAN

By pressing a button on his suit, Scott Lang can shrink to be Ant-Man or grow to be Giant-Man. Put the pictures in size order, from the smallest to the biggest.

SMALLEST - - - - - - - - - - - - - - - - - - -> BIGGEST

Answers on page 30

SYMBOL SEQUENCES

The Avengers all have their own super symbol. Whose symbol is needed to complete each sequence below? Draw your answers in the circles.

A

B

C

D

E

Answers on page 30

HULK SMASH!

Oops! Hulk didn't like this picture of himself, so he smashed it. Match the pieces to the spaces to work out which piece is not from the picture.

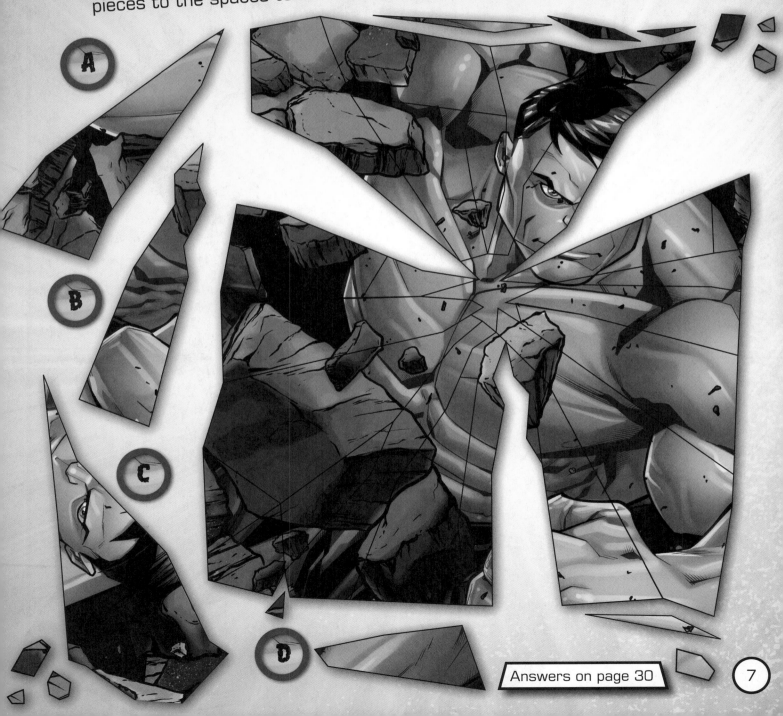

Answers on page 30

VISION'S VISIONS

Vision can process information at superhuman speed. How quickly can you work out which six Avengers he is picturing in his amazing mind?
ONE, TWO, GO!

1. GOES GREEN WHEN ANGERED.

Vision is thinking of ....

2. KNOWN AS THE SON OF ODIN.

Vision is thinking of ....

3. EXPERT IN THE WORLD OF ESPIONAGE.

Vision is thinking of ....

4. CARRIES A VIBRANIUM SHIELD.

Vision is thinking of ....

5. INVENTOR WITH GENIUS-LEVEL INTELLECT.

Vision is thinking of ....

6. WEARS A HIGH-TECH WINGED HARNESS.

Vision is thinking of ....

Answers on page 30

All The Arrows

Super-shot archer Hawkeye needs to refill his quiver. How many arrows can you count below, plus the one in his bow?

Write your answer here.

....

Answers on page 30

In The Eye

The Eye of Agamotto is all-seeing. Complete this dot-to-dot of the Sorcerer Supreme, Doctor Strange. Then, colour him in!

10

SEEING RED

Red Skull is the fearsome leader of the Hydra army. Can you spot six differences between these pictures of Cap's evil enemy?

Answers on page 30

HULK VS HULKBUSTER

The Hulk is in a rage, so the Hulkbuster has been sent to stop him. Find a path for each big guy so they will meet in the middle.

SMASH!

Answers on page 31

EYES ON THE BAD GUYS

Hawkeye has three fearsome foes in his sights. Can you match each close-up to the correct evil enemy? Draw lines to link them.

LOKI

RED SKULL

ULTRON

A

B

C

D

E

F

CROUCH AND POUNCE

These three heroes are practising their crouch-and-pounce poses.
Look closely at the shadows and circle the odd one out.

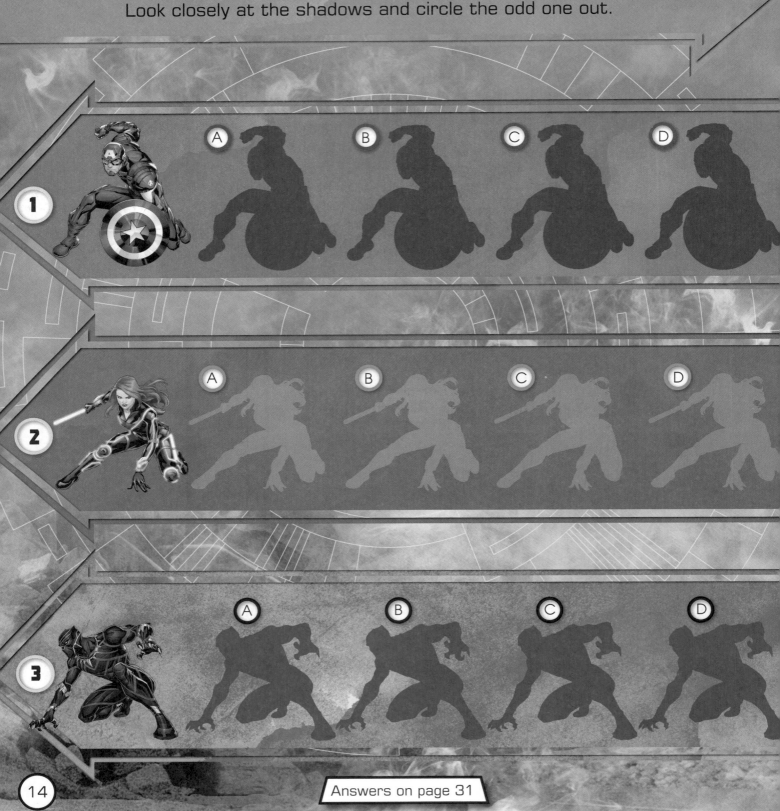

Answers on page 31

FAST AND FURIOUS

Nick Fury, Director of S.H.I.E.L.D., always comes out fighting when the going gets tough. Can you find six differences between these two pictures?

Answers on page 31

SHURI'S SHADOW

Shuri is a Wakandan princess and a fearless warrior. Which shadow exactly matches the picture of Black Panther's sister?

Answers on page 31

SO MANY SHIELDS

Captain America has lost his shield among lots of fakes. See if you can spot the following among the rows, plus Cap's real shield:

1. The upside-down shield.
2. The smallest shield.
3. The biggest shield. This is Cap's shield.
4. The shield with a missing star.

Answers on page 31

DAY AND NIGHT FLIGHT

Trouble never sleeps so the Avengers are on call day and night. Use the stickers from your sticker sheets to add some flying heroes soaring into these scenes.

BEST BUDS

Steve Rogers will always be there for his pal Bucky Barnes. Lead Cap to the Winter Soldier by picking the path that adds up to 15.

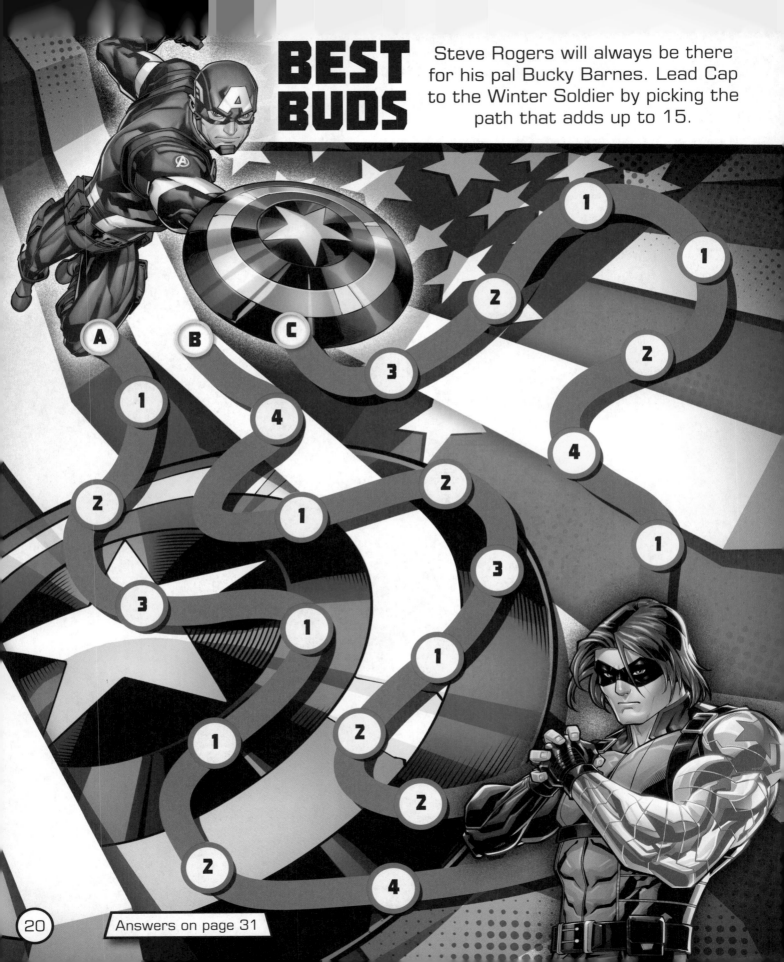

Answers on page 31

AWESOME A.I.

Ultron can infiltrate almost any computer network. Can you spot the sequence below that matches the code he is attempting to crack? Put a tick next to your answer.

Computer code:
BAALKJXKYYYFMCO

1) BAAJKLXKYYYFMCO

2) BAALKJXKYKYMFCO

3) BAAKLJXKYYFYMCO

4) BAALKJXKYYYFMCO

5) BAALKJKXYYYFMOC

Answers on page 31

PERFECT WARRIOR

Foes beware, fierce warrior Okoye will fight for her country and her king. Only one of the smaller images exactly matches the bigger picture. Can you spot which one?

A

B

C

D

E

Answers on page 31

FLIGHT FOR GOOD

Using the icon key below, help Wasp find her way to Ant-Man.

KEY

| UP | DOWN | LEFT | RIGHT |

START

FINISH

Answers on page 31

MISCHIEF COLOURS

Loki, Prince of Asgard, loves to cause trouble for his brother, Thor. Add colour to Odin's scheming adopted son, with his horned helmet and magic sceptre.

SPOT T'CHALLA

Black Panther, the mighty martial arts expert, is always ready to pounce. Which box is missing a picture of him?

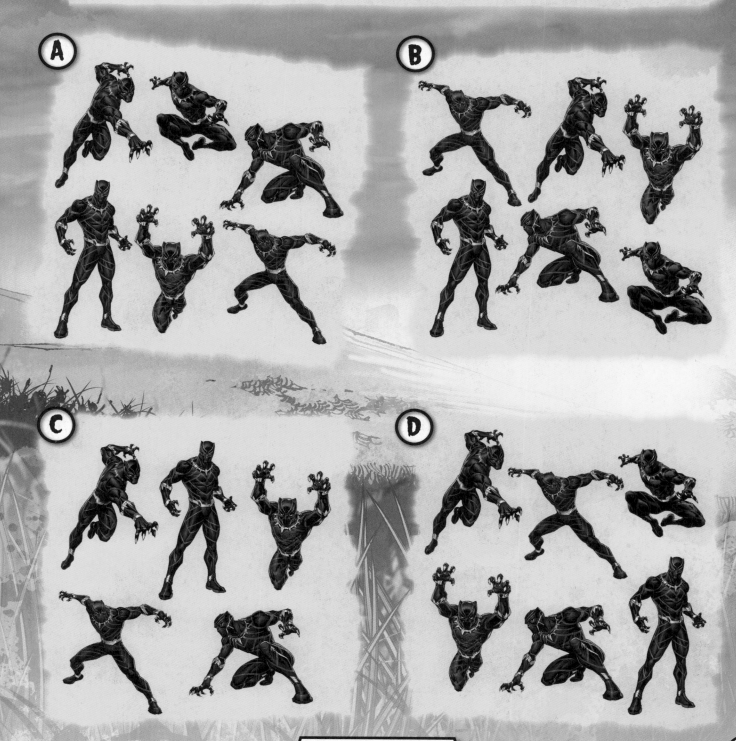

A

B

C

D

Answers on page 31

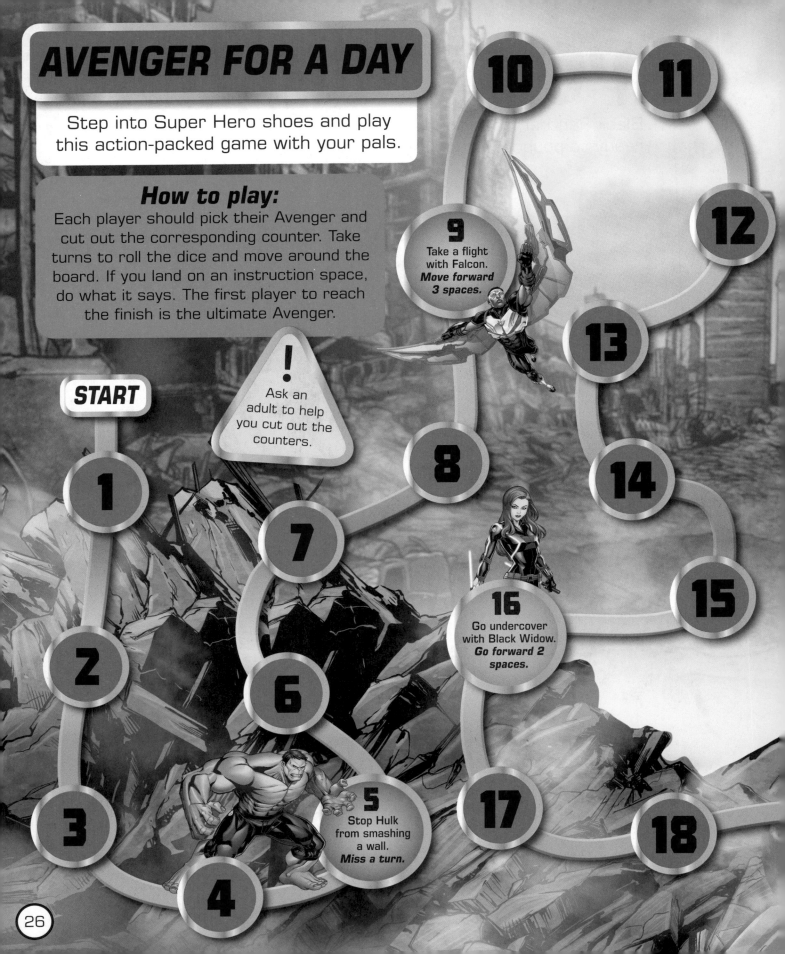

AVENGER FOR A DAY

Step into Super Hero shoes and play this action-packed game with your pals.

How to play:

Each player should pick their Avenger and cut out the corresponding counter. Take turns to roll the dice and move around the board. If you land on an instruction space, do what it says. The first player to reach the finish is the ultimate Avenger.

! Ask an adult to help you cut out the counters.

START

9 Take a flight with Falcon. *Move forward 3 spaces.*

16 Go undercover with Black Widow. *Go forward 2 spaces.*

5 Stop Hulk from smashing a wall. *Miss a turn.*

10 11 12 13 14 15 8 7 6 17 18 1 2 3 4

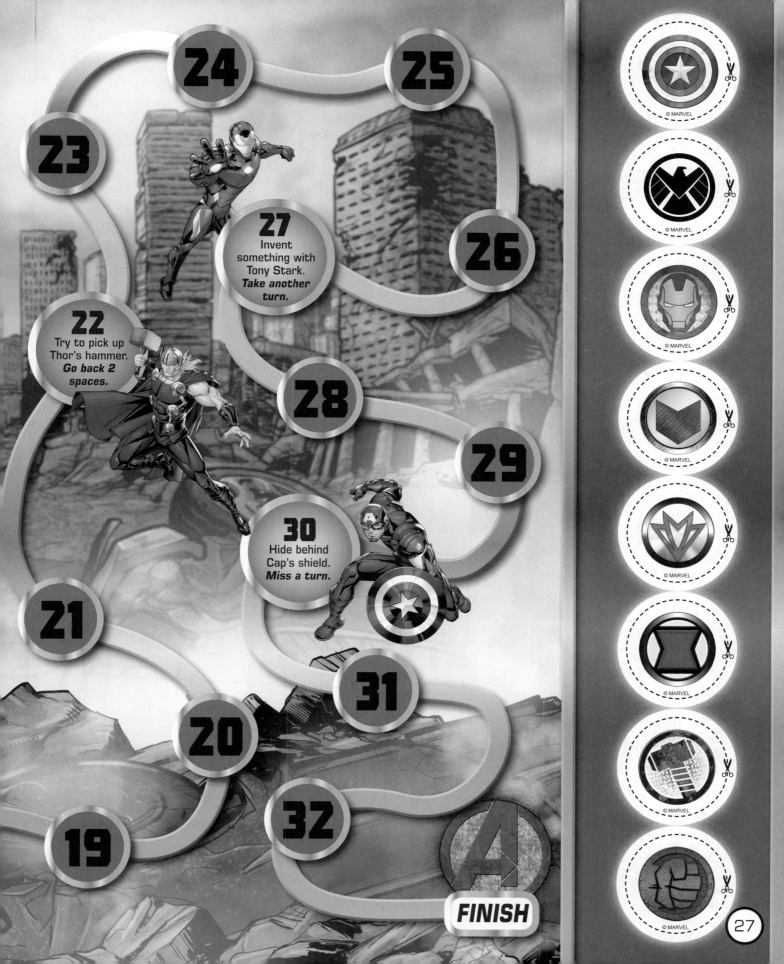

24

25

23

27
Invent
something with
Tony Stark.
*Take another
turn.*

26

22
Try to pick up
Thor's hammer.
*Go back 2
spaces.*

28

29

30
Hide behind
Cap's shield.
Miss a turn.

21

31

20

19

32

FINISH

© MARVEL

© MARVEL

© MARVEL

© MARVEL

© MARVEL

© MARVEL

© MARVEL

© MARVEL

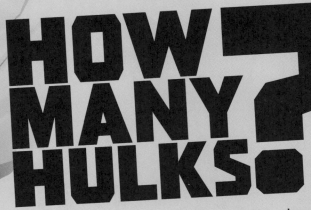

HOW MANY HULKS?

It can be tricky to blend in when you're big and green. How many times can you spot the word **'HULK'** hiding in the grid?

H	U	K	L	U	H
H	U	L	H	K	U
U	K	U	U	K	L
L	L	H	L	L	K
K	U	U	K	U	U
H	H	U	L	H	H

ANSWER

Answers on page 31

MASK TASK

Copy this picture of Iron Man's mask, using the grid lines to help you, then colour it in.

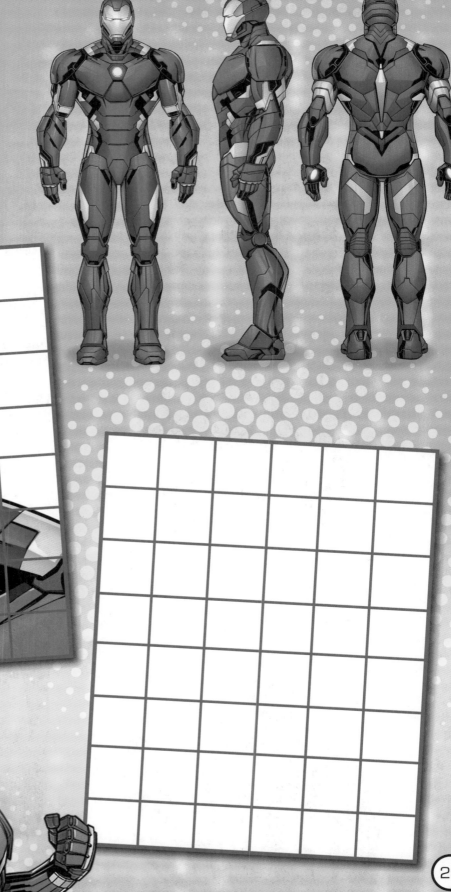

ANSWERS

Page 2

Page 3

Page 4
A-4, B-3, C-2, D-1

Page 5
E, D, C, B, F, A

Page 6

Page 7
D is not part of the picture

Page 8
1. Hulk 2. Thor 3. Black Widow
4. Captain America 5. Iron Man 6. Falcon

Page 9
There are 22 arrows

Page 11

ANSWERS

Page 12

Page 13
Loki — C+F, Red Skull — B+D, Ultron — A+E

Page 14
1-D, 2-C, 3-B

Page 15

Page 16
Shadow C matches exactly

Page 17

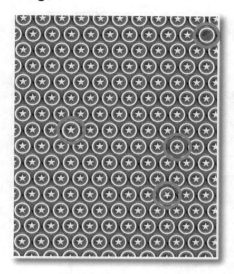

Page 20
Line B adds up to 15

Page 21
Code 4 is the correct code

Page 22
Picture D matches exactly

Page 23

Page 25
Box C is missing a Panther

Page 28
'HULK' appears 8 times

EARTH'S
MIGHTIEST
HEROES